THIS BOOK BELONGS TO

_____

Have questions? We want to hear from you!
Email us at: support@activitywizo.com

Please consider writing a review!
Just visit: activitywizo.com/review

FREE BONUS

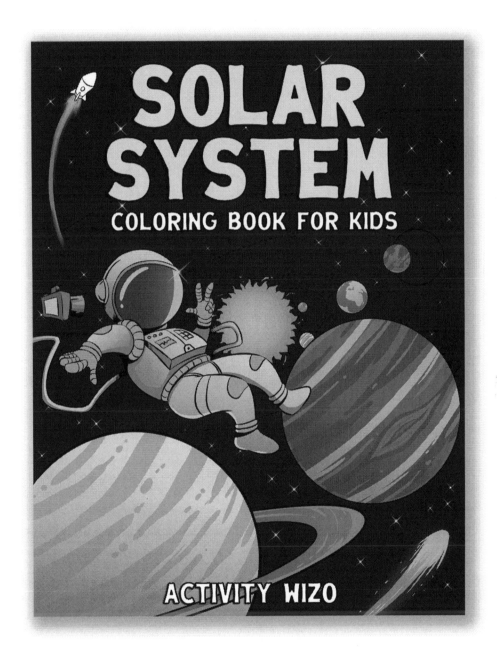

Just flip to the end of the book to get the link!

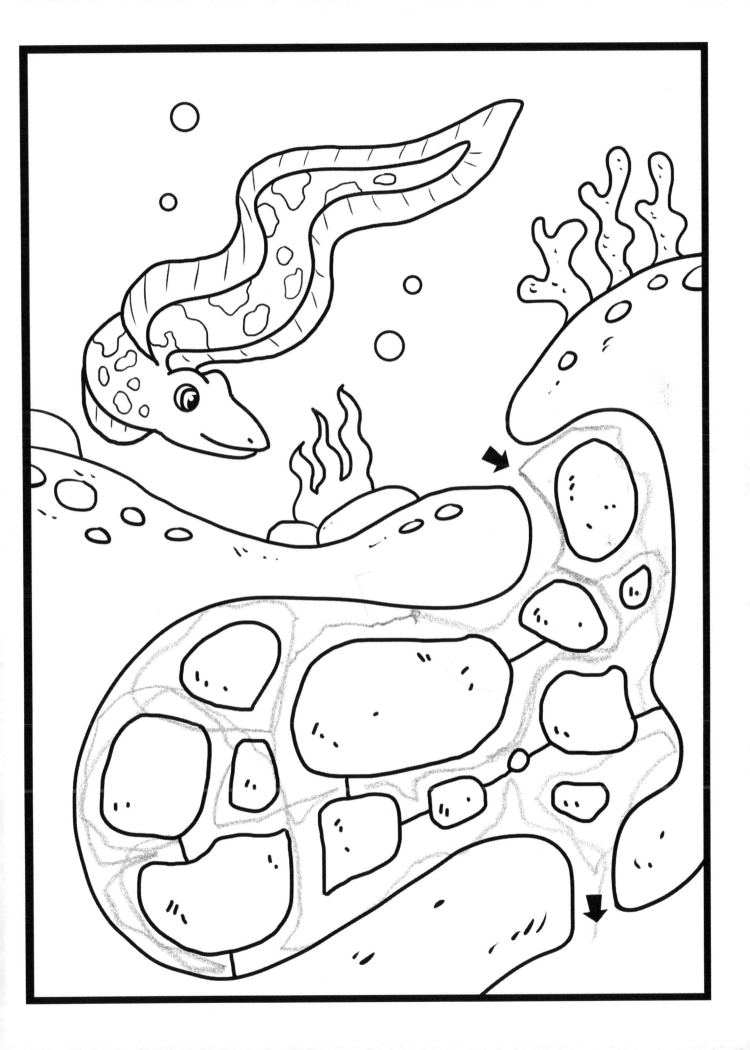

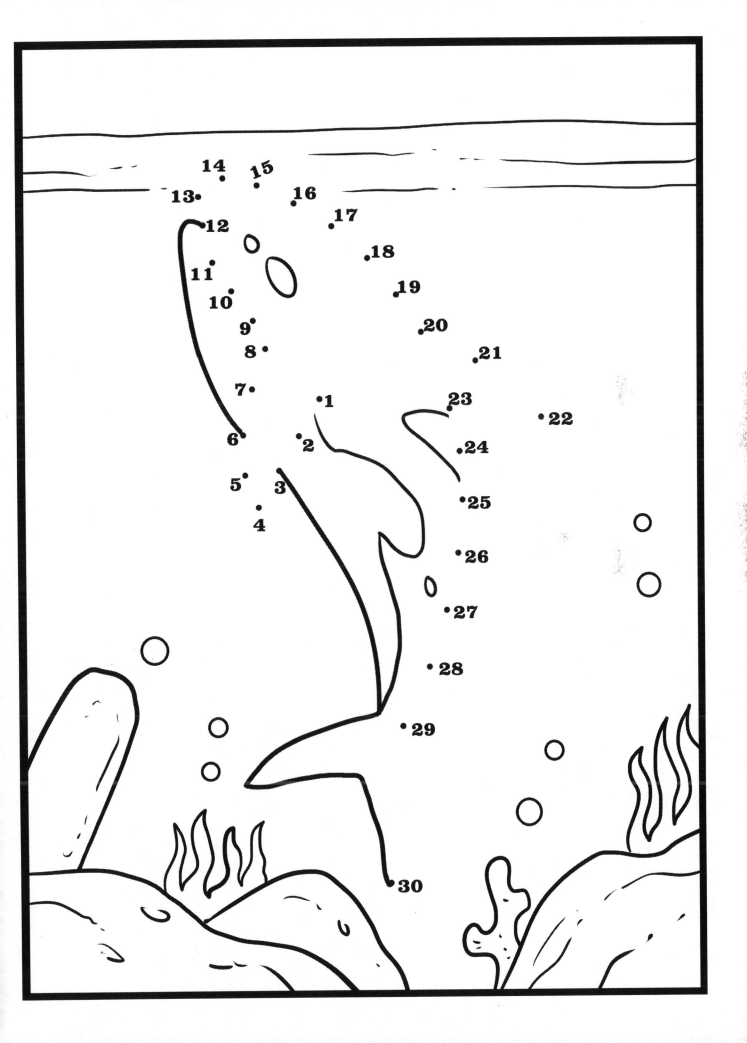

ANSWER KEY

ANSWER KEY

ANSWER KEY

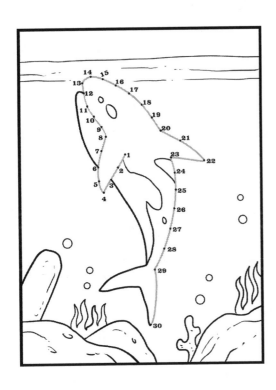

FREE BONUS

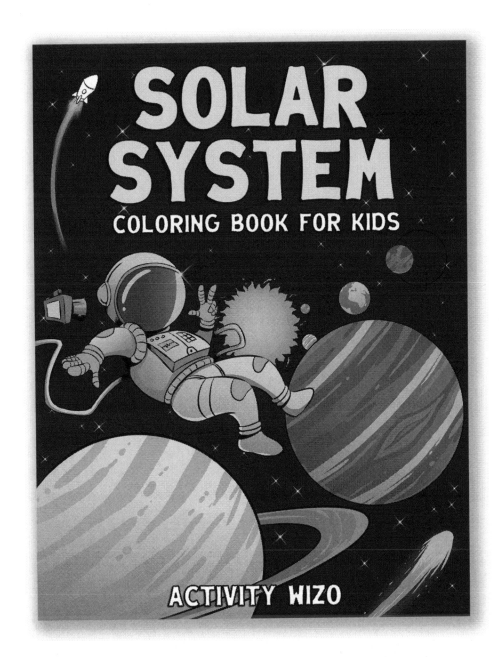

Get This FREE Bonus Now!

Just go to: activitywizo.com/free

Made in the USA
Middletown, DE
28 December 2020